The Book of Possibility

Courtney Cox Smith

swallowtail books
houston

For Wyatt

ISBN 978-0-578-62518-8

Library of Congress Control Number: 2019920488

First Printing 2019

swallowtail books

www.swallowtailbooks.com

Come, my friends,
'Tis not too late to seek a newer world.
Push off, and sitting well in order smite
The surrounding furrows; for my purpose holds
To sail beyond the sunset, and the baths
of all the western stars, until I die.
It may be that the gulfs will wash us down;
It may be we shall touch the Happy Isles,
And see the great Achilles, whom we knew.
Though much is taken, much abides; and though
We are not now that strength which in old days
Moved earth and heaven; that which we are, we are;
One equal temper of heroic hearts,
Made weak by time and fate, but strong in will
To strive, to seek, to find, and not to yield.

-Alfred, Lord Tennyson

Sometimes,
the world is a place of
meanness,
cruelty,
loneliness,
and pain.

What if we choose...

Every person has the ability to be kind. Kindness needs only a willing heart.

We may feel
scared,
fearful,
uncertain,
or anxious.

What if we choose...

COURAGE

Even the bravest person feels fear. Courage is when we choose to keep going.

We may witness
indifference
or harshness
when others
struggle or hurt.

What if we choose...

Compassion

Compassion is the gentle comfort of another human being reminding us that we are not alone.

We may see
greed and selfishness
while others
suffer in poverty.

What if we choose...

Generosity requires only a giving spirit, helping hands, and
a desire to put another's need ahead of our own.

Some days, we will feel
weighed-down,
overwhelmed,
or bored.

What if we choose...

wonder

A life without wonder is like a night without stars.
To live in wonder is to stand in grateful awe
of the smallest and simplest pieces of life.

We may experience
sadness,
disappointment,
or worry.

What if we choose...

Joy is the convergence of love and gratitude that bursts from within us when we connect the deepest desires of our hearts with the experience of our lives.

We will face
conflict,
anger,
and frustration.

What if we choose...

PEACE

Peace is the ability to breathe in the possibility and newness of each day as we trust that no matter what may come, all will be well.

Some days,
darkness may threaten
to drown the light,
and we may feel
despair,
sorrow,
or doubt.

What if we choose...

Hope is knowing that light always finds a way through the darkness.

For reasons
hard to understand,
we may experience
bitterness,
loneliness,
or hate.

What if we choose...

LOVE

Love is the answer to all things, good or bad.
No matter what we experience in life, we can choose love.

**Show love,
feel love,
share love,
become love.**

What if...

What a world we could be.

Visit the Swallowtail Books website to download your free Book of Possibility 30-Day Challenge Bundle.

A companion to The Book of Possibility, the bundle includes three separate 30-Day challenges encouraging kindness, generosity, and wonder.

www.swallowtailbooks.com

Be sure to check out our other titles, latest news, and forthcoming publications.

Thank you for purchasing The Book of Possibility.

swallowtail books

Building a better world, one book at a time.

Made in the USA
Columbia, SC
09 June 2020